Electronic Projects in Music

G000300766

Other Constructor's Projects Books

Electronic Projects in Music

A. J. Flind
Series Editor Philip Chapman

Newnes Technical Books

The Butterworth Group

United Kingdom	**Butterworth & Co (Publishers) Ltd** London: 88 Kingsway, WC2B 6AB
Australia	**Butterworths Pty Ltd** Sydney: 586 Pacific Highway, Chatswood, NSW2067 Also at Melbourne, Brisbane, Adelaide and Perth
Canada	**Butterworth & Co (Canada) Ltd** Toronto: 2265 Midland Avenue, Scarborough, Ontario M1P 4S1
New Zealand	**Butterworths of New Zealand Ltd** Wellington: T & W Young Building, 77—85 Customhouse Quay, 1, CPO Box 472
South Africa	**Butterworth & Co (South Africa) (Pty) Ltd** Durban: 152—154 Gale Street
USA	**Butterworth (Publishers) Inc** Boston: 10 Tower Office Park, Woburn, Mass. 01801

First published 1979 by Newnes Technical Books
a Butterworth imprint

© Butterworth & Co (Publishers) Ltd, 1979

British Library Cataloguing in Publication Data

Flind, A J
    Electronic projects in music.
    1. Electronic apparatus and appliances — Amateurs'
    manuals
    2. Sound — Apparatus
    I. Title
    681'.8   TK9965   78-40953

    ISBN 0 408 00391 X

Typeset by Butterworths Litho Preparation Department

Printed in England by William Clowes & Sons Ltd
Beccles and London

Preface

This book is intended for both the newcomer to electronics and for those with a little experience. Most of the projects are very simple to construct and should present no problems even to an absolute beginner, though a little practice with some of the simpler circuits of the first few chapters would be advisable before tackling the more complex ones towards the end.

Many of the projects have a general appeal. The preamps, mixer and the amplifier of project 13 will all find a host of uses whilst the mini organ in project 11 should delight anyone, whether musically minded or not.

All the projects in this book use widely available components obtainable almost anywhere. They are all built on standard size pieces of Veroboard, a sort of general purpose printed circuit board, to make construction as simple as possible. Very few tools are required: a small pair of sharp-nosed pliers, sidecutters, wire strippers, and a soldering iron with a 3mm ($^1/_8$ in) bit are all that are absolutely necessary. The only item of test equipment that is really indispensable is a reasonable quality test meter.

Though these projects are intended for beginners, performance has not been sacrificed for the sake of simplicity; many of the guitar effects have performances equal to the best commercially available equivalents. Despite this, the projects in this book are all relatively inexpensive to build, and should provide a valuable demonstration of how much money one can save by making one's own special effects equipment.

Contents

1

Guitar Preamp

This simple low cost circuit may be used to boost the output of a guitar pickup to a level suitable for feeding an insensitive amplifier; it will also be found useful for matching many other types of signal source to inputs of different sensitivities. A disco preamp, for example, may be found to have an output which is too low to drive the power amplifier with which it is intended to be used; the inclusion of this simple stage, possibly with a gain of only two or three, may be all that is required to correct matters.

The circuit

This type of circuit (Fig. 1.1) is known as a 'class A' amplifier stage, and is the simplest of the amplifiers. It has a continuous current flow

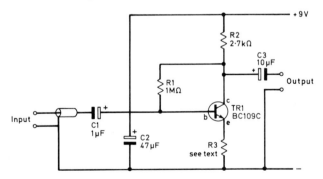

Figure 1.1

Guitar preamp circuit

through the active device, in this case TR1, which is varied up or down by the input signal. Consider the circuit with no input signal applied.

A constant small input current, known as 'bias' flows into the base of TR1 through resistor R1. A transistor obtains its gain from the fact that a small current flowing into its base causes a much larger current to flow from the emitter to the collector. Thus this bias current causes a current to pass through TR1 and the 'load' resistor R2, so a constant d.c. voltage appears at the collector. The bias is taken from the collector, rather than the positive supply, to help stabilise the operating point of the circuit, as transistor gains vary widely both with different examples of the same type, and with changes of temperature. A rise, for example, in the current flowing through TR1 due to a gain change, will produce a drop in the voltage at the collector, leading to a drop in the bias current which tends to restore the circuit to its correct operating point.

If an audio signal is now applied to the base of TR1 through the d.c. blocking capacitor C1, it will result in an audio frequency variation in the current passing into the base. This results in a much larger variation in the current flowing through the collector and R2, and a consequently large audio variation appears in the voltage at the collector, from which the output is taken.

If the maximum possible gain is required, the emitter of TR1 may be taken directly to the negative supply rail. However, it may be that only a limited amount of gain is needed for a particular application, and more would produce problems of noise and perhaps instability. If this is the case, the gain of this circuit may be conveniently controlled by introducing R3, the emitter resistor, which provides a form of negative feedback. As the signal voltage varies, so the changing current drawn through R3 causes a voltage to appear at the emitter which tends to follow the signal and thus reduce the amplitude of signal current flow into the base.

Capacitor C2 is known as a 'decoupling' capacitor; its purpose is to smooth out small variations in the supply voltage caused by the changes in the current drawn by TR1.

Construction

Construction of this simple little circuit is very easy and should pose no problems even for the absolute beginner. It is built on a piece of 0.1in pitch matrix board with ten strips of 24 holes (Fig. 1.2), a standard size available from most suppliers. Note the single cut required in one of the strips (Fig. 1.3), which may be made either with the proper strip cutting tool (a worthwhile investment) or with a small twist drill bit. Take care to assemble the components correctly and observe the capacitor polarities.

The value of R3 can be selected from Table 1.1 for the use to which the preamp is to be put, an alternative if required might be to fit a 1kΩ preset and adjust the gain as required after assembly.

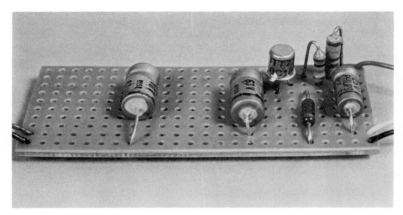

Figure 1.2

Photograph of assembled board

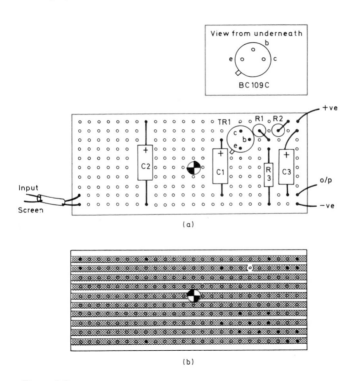

(a)

(b)

Figure 1.3

Guitar preamp board (a) Component layout (b) Copper side

Once the unit is built, it is a good idea to check carefully through it against the circuit diagram, starting from the input and following through the signal path. Any construction errors will usually be readily

Table 1.1. Variation of gain for various values of R3

R3 (Ω)	Voltage gain	Gain (dB)
0	100	40
10	70	37
18	50	34
47	30	30
100	20	26
220	10	20
470	5	14
1000	2	6

apparent if this is done. Testing is straightforward; with the device connected to the input of the amplifier with which it is to be used, an input can be applied and the increase in gain should be apparent. If it doesn't work, recheck the construction, make sure the break in the copper strip is in the right place, and finally check the d.c. voltage at TR1 collector. This will vary a bit due to different transistor gains and values of R3, but it should be somewhere in the range 4–7 volts. If it lies outside this there is definitely a fault present. Details of component testing methods will be given later.

The power requirements of this unit are very small, around 1mA, so the power can be supplied either from a small 9V battery such as a PP3 or from the power rail of the equipment with which it is to be used if this is of the right polarity, using an appropriate dropping resistor to reduce the voltage if necessary to 9V.

Using the preamp

This simple assembly may be mounted with a single screw passing through a hole drilled in the board, using an insulating spacer – a small rubber grommet would do – to prevent the copper strips coming into contact with anything conductive. Care should be taken to see that the screw does not touch the strips and cause short circuits between them if there is any liklihood of this happening they can be broken either side of the screw. The unit can be mounted inside the equipment with which it is to be used, or if it is to be separately powered it might be placed inside the instrument it is intended to amplify, say, behind the

4

fingerboard of a guitar with a low output pickup. Input and output leads should ideally be kept as short as possible; if they are of any appreciable length screened lead should be used to keep hum pickup to a minimum.

Components for the guitar preamp

Resistors
R1   1MΩ
R2   2.7kΩ
R3   See Table 1.1

Capacitors
C1   1μF, 10V electrolytic
C2   47μF, 10V electrolytic
C3   10μF, 10V electrolytic

Semiconductors
TR1   BC109C

Miscellaneous
Matrix board 0.1in pitch, 10 strips by 24 holes

2

Microphone Preamp

This project is very similar to the preceding guitar preamp, save for one important difference. The simple amplifier stage of the last chapter has one drawback, in that its input impedance, or resistance to the a.c. input signal, is relatively low, of the order of $20k\Omega$ or less. It is also to some extent dependent upon the value of the emitter resistor, so that the higher the gain required, the lower the input impedance becomes. This is no problem with low impedance sources such as a magnetic guitar pickup, but a device such as a crystal microphone, which gives a very small voltage output from a very high internal impedance, renders the single transistor stage almost useless on its own. Various circuits can be employed to overcome this defect, but the simplest is probably that used in this project: the use of a field effect transistor (FET) as a source follower to buffer the input signal before it reaches the transistor stage.

Circuit action

Referring to Fig. 2.1, the part of the circuit around TR2 is identical to that of the guitar preamp. It uses the same component values, and in fact provides the same gain, depending upon the value selected for R5. The FET contributes no voltage gain to the circuit, and is there simply to provide input buffering and raise the input impedance.

An FET works on somewhat different principles to an ordinary 'bipolar' transistor. It consists essentially of a single bar of semiconductor material, with the ends known as 'source' and 'drain'. This bar would normally act as a simple resistor, but near the middle is a junction with semiconductor material of opposite polarity, known as the 'gate'. Reverse biasing this junction results in the build-up of a charged area around it known as the 'depletion layer' through which the current in the bar cannot flow; this tends to reduce the current somewhat. The

6

size of the depletion layer, and the current flow through the bar, depends upon the amount of reverse bias applied; if this is sufficient the current may be stopped altogether, this condition being known as 'pinch-off'. Thus unlike the transistor, which is 'off' until biased 'on' by

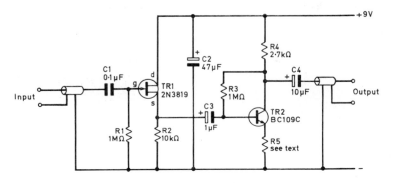

Figure 2.1
Microphone preamp circuit

a small current passing through its forward biased base, the FET is 'on' until biased 'off' by a reverse voltage bias at its gate. The fact that this junction is reverse biased and not forward as with the transistor gives the FET its very high input impedance — often many tens of megohms.

Enough of the technology! To bias TR1, in the circuit of Fig. 2.1, a high value resistor (R1) is connected from gate to ground. The current passing through TR1 and R2 causes the voltage at the source to rise above that on the gate, increasing the reverse bias until it is high enough to prevent any further increase in current flow. Thus the voltage at the source will assume a steady value. Any change in the voltage at the gate, such as that produced by an audio signal passing through C1, will produce an equal change in the voltage at the source, at the much lower impedance of R2. Signal from the source is taken through C3 to TR2 for amplification and passes from TR2 collector to output. Note that due to the very high input impedance only a small (0.1μF) capacitor is required to couple the signal source to TR1 gate.

Construction

Construction is again on a piece of matrix board of 10 strips of 24 holes each (Fig. 2.2), and follows to some extent the layout of the previous project. If necessary it would with care be possible to modify the previous project to obtain the higher impedance of this version. Note

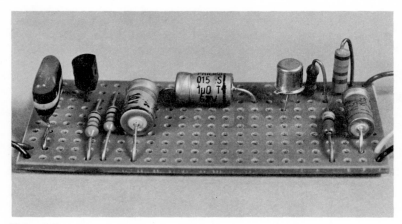

Figure 2.2

Photograph of assembled board

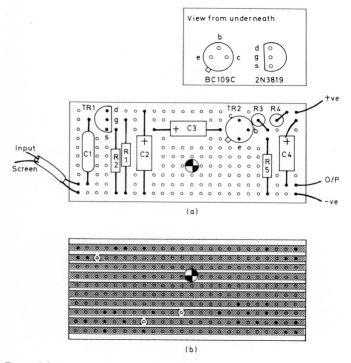

(a)

(b)

Figure 2.3

Matrix board (a) Component layout (b) Copper side

8

that if this is done the polarity of C3 is reversed. Three breaks are required in the copper strips (Fig. 2.3). Table 1.1 should be used to select the value of R5 for the gain required. It is good practice to solder the FET in place last, and to avoid handling it, particularly the gate lead, any more than necessary. Once again after construction it is a good plan to check through the circuit to ensure there are no mistakes. If there are no faults in construction the unit should work first time; if not the d.c. voltage check at TR2 collector is the same as in the previous project. There should also be a voltage present at the source of the FET; differing FET characteristics make it impossible to specify exactly what voltage should be present, but somewhere between 2 and 5V should be correct.

The power used by the circuit is again very low, and a PP3 battery will give many hours' use, or the unit may be powered from the equipment with which it is to be used, using a resistor to reduce the supply to 9V if necessary.

Using the preamp

As with the guitar preamp the unit may be mounted by means of a single screw and a spacer. It may be incorporated into the amplifier with which it is to be used, but due to the high impedance of the input if there is to be any appreciable length of cable between the signal

Components list for the microphone preamp

Resistors
R1   1MΩ
R2   10kΩ
R3   1MΩ
R4   2.7kΩ
R5   See text

Capacitors
C1   0.1μF polyester
C2   47μF, 10V electrolytic
C3   1μF, 10V electrolytic
C4   10μF, 10V electrolytic

Semiconductors
TR1   2N3819
TR2   BC109C

Miscellaneous
Matrix board 0.1in pitch, 10 strips by 24 holes

source and the amplifier it would be much better if it were placed at the signal end. A unit such as this is frequently used, in fact, to reduce the output impedance of a microphone simply so that a long length of cable may be used between it and the main amplifier without excessive hum pick-up. In such a case it is usual to try and incorporate it actually inside the microphone case, with a small battery to make it self-powered. The use of screened lead to the input is essential.

3

Metronome

This simple but interesting little project will serve to assist budding musicians to practise keeping a constant tempo. Though pocket-sized and inexpensive, it nonetheless produces clicks at least as loud as its traditional mechanical counterpart, over a wide range of frequencies.

The circuit

A look at Fig. 3.1 shows that this project is simplicity itself. It relies for this simplicity on the action of TR1, a unijunction transistor, used in a circuit configuration called a relaxation oscillator.

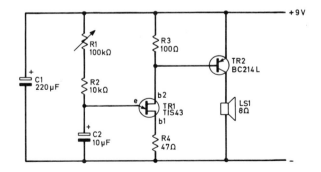

Figure 3.1

Metronome circuit

The unijunction, like the FET, is another single junction device, but its action in a circuit is somewhat different. In the arrangement shown, when the supply is initially switched on, it passes only a small leakage current between two of its terminals, called base 1 and base 2, and no current at all flows through its emitter. Thus C2 starts to charge up through R1 and R2, and the voltage on the emitter begins to rise. When this voltage is high enough, somewhere between a half and two thirds of the supply voltage, the emitter junction suddenly breaks down, causing C2 to discharge rapidly through b1 and R4. Whilst this discharge is taking place conduction also occurs between b1 and b2, via the current limiting resistor R3. Once C2 has discharged, the emitter again becomes non-conductive, current ceases to flow through b1 and b2, and C2 commences to charge again. The output of the device thus consists of very short positive going pulses at b1, equally short negative going pulses at b2, and a high impedance sawtooth waveform at the emitter. The frequency, or pulse repetition rate, is almost entirely dependent upon the value of C2 and its charging resistors, so by making one of these variable (R1) a wide range of frequencies can be generated. In this circuit R2 is used to set the maximum rate.

The unijunction itself cannot handle enough current to produce a click of sufficient volume, so TR2 is employed in a switching mode to do this. It is a *pnp* type, which means that, although it works in exactly the same manner as the *npn* type BC109C used in previous projects, its polarities are reversed. Thus the emitter is connected to the positive supply, and with its base also connected to positive through R3 it remains switched off and passes no current. When TR1 becomes conductive, however, the negative pulse from b2 causes TR2 to switch hard on, and for the very short duration of the pulse it passes almost full supply voltage to the speaker, resulting in a very loud click.

Though the average current drawn by the circuit is small, for the short duration of each click, whilst TR2 is switched on, a very heavy current of around 300mA is drawn. A small battery such as the PP3 is incapable of supplying this sort of power, so the capacitor C1 is used to store energy between pulses and supply it when required.

Construction

Once again a piece of 0.1in pitch matrix board with ten strips of 24 holes each is used. TR1 and TR2 are both plastics types, marked by a flat on one side (Fig. 3.2); care should be taken to see that they are fitted the right way round. The lead connection drawings (Fig. 3.3) show them as if one were looking at them from the leadout side, i.e. holding them upside down. Capacitor C2 is a tantalum bead type, employed in this circuit for its low leakage properties, and it is polarised, so care should be taken as with normal electrolytics to fit it the right way round. They are generally marked with a very small + printed on one side above the positive lead. The potentiometer, R1 is shown with

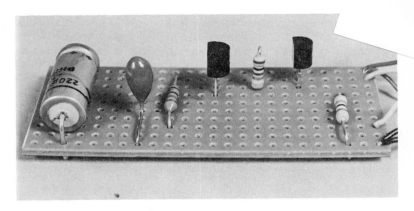

Figure 3.2

Photograph of assembled components

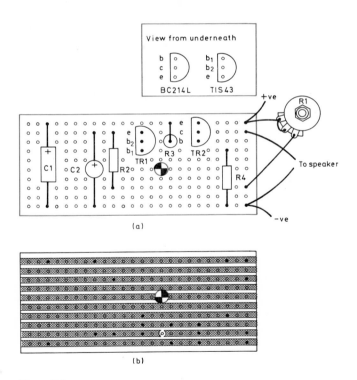

Figure 3.3

Metronome board (a) Component layout (b) Copper side

two tags strapped together; this again is the conventional way of doing things; the centre tag could just as easily be used on its own.

Once again the completed assembly should be checked out against the circuit diagram and if all is well it may be tested. There is little that can stop a circuit as simple as this from operating, but if trouble is experienced a sensitive voltmeter (20kΩ/V or better) may be used to check that C2 is charging if TR1 emitter is disconnected and R1 reduced to its minimum value, and a pair of headphones should be able to pick up the pulse between base 1 and ground (across R4), also between base 2 and positive, (across R3).

The unit may easily be built into a pocket-sized case, either home-made or one of the better looking plastics cases now widely available. A 2 or 3 inch speaker can be used and it will be found that the case imparts a resonance to the short 'clicks' which make them appear far louder and give them a quality astonishingly like the sound of a mechanical metronome. The current consumption varies slightly according to the frequency in use, but is never more than 10mA, so a PP3 battery will last a long time. A separate on-off switch may be used, perhaps a small slide switch, or R1 may be of the type fitted with a switch. A pointer knob will be needed, fitted over a glued-on paper dial, on which calibration marks may be inked in, using either a watch or another metronome as a reference. The finished dial can be covered with clear self-adhesive plastic to give a good appearance.

Using the metronome

This project should prove invaluable to anyone learning to play an instrument. It will also find other applications in timing, etc., since it

Components list for the metronome

Resistors
R1   100kΩ linear pot
R2   10kΩ
R3   100Ω
R4   47Ω

Capacitors
C1   220μF, 10V electrolytic
C2   10μF, 10V tantalum bead type

Semiconductors
TR1   TIS43
TR2   BC214L

Miscellaneous
Miniature loudspeaker (8Ω)
Matrix board, 0.1in pitch, 10 strips by 24 holes
Switch SPST, case etc. as required

may readily be set up to count seconds, and it will also be found very effective for keeping small children amused for short periods! A small point worth mentioning is that it will continue to tick for a second or two after switch-off; this is normal and is due to the discharge of the energy stored in C1.

4

Treble Booster

This unit, intended primarily for use with electric guitars, gives a boost to the higher frequencies and harmonics produced by that instrument. The result is a striking, 'brilliant' sound, the degree of which can be varied by means of a single control. Inputs or controls to produce this effect are sometimes found on better class p.a. amplifiers, generally labelled 'brilliance', or 'presence'. This simple project can be incorporated easily into the cheapest amplifier to achieve the same effect.

The circuit

From Fig. 4.1 it will be seen that the circuit employs two transistors.

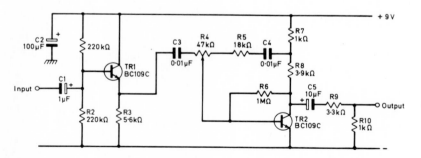

Figure 4.1

Treble boost circuit

The first acts simply as a buffer to convert the medium impedance input required by the guitar pickup into the low impedance drive necessary for the correct operation of the boost network. The operation of this stage is similar to the FET preamp stage described earlier, although the use of a transistor means that the biasing arrangements are a little different.

From the emitter of TR1 the buffered signal passes to the actual booster network based around TR2. C3, C4, R4 and R5 comprise this network. Consider R4 with its wiper at the C3 end of its travel. A capacitor exhibits reactance, or opposition, to the passage of an a.c. signal, but this reactance decreases with rising frequency. C3 is chosen to pass the frequencies it is required to boost, and partially attenuate lower ones. Thus these frequencies are passed straight to TR2 base for amplification and arrive at the collector with a fair degree of boost. Now consider the same circuit with the pot wiper at the other end of its travel, towards R5. The signal can still reach TR2 base, but now it will be easily modified by any signal coming back from the collector through C4. A transistor connected as a common-emitter amplifier, like TR2, causes a phase reversal of the signal passing through it, that is, the positive halves of the input signal appear at the collector as negative going and vice-versa, so any feedback from collector to base becomes negative feedback and tends to cancel the signal at the input. Once again the higher frequencies are selected, this time by C4, so only the high frequencies passed by C3 tend to be partially cancelled. Thus the transistor amplifies less effectively at higher frequencies, so these pass with only a small gain, whilst the lower frequencies receive more amplification and are restored to their level before attenuation by C3. By careful selection of component values the circuit can be designed to give from a virtually flat frequency response at one end of the pot travel to several dB of boost for the higher frequencies at the other.

The circuit exhibits a small overall gain; with this type of device it is an advantage if the overall gain is unity, so that on stage the effect can be switched in or out as required without any adjustment to volume being necessary, so R9 and R10 form an attenuator to return the output to the correct level. These can be omitted and the output taken straight from C5 if this feature is not required.

Construction

This project uses a larger size of matrix board (Fig. 4.2), the same 0.1in pitch, but with 24 strips of 37 holes. So construction is rather less compact. Slightly more care will be found necessary however, to ensure that the component leads are inserted into the right holes. Two cuts are needed in the copper strips (Fig. 4.3). Two links are necessary with this design, 22s.w.g. bare tinned copper wire is best for this, though by no means essential, almost any wire will do. Remember the sequence; links first, then the resistors, then capacitors, finally fit the transistors;

construction in this order will make life much easier. A word of warning; it's surprisingly easy to break the leads off the stripy polyester capacitors, so bend these with great care. Note that TR2 fits on the board the opposite way up to TR1. The finished board may be built into an amplifier and connected to provide 'brilliance' as is the case with some commercial amplifiers, using either a separate input jack or a switch to cut it in and out of use. Or it may be built as a separate self-powered unit with a plug and socket to simply plug it in series between a guitar and its amplifier. The power needed to run it is only around 3mA, so again a PP3 battery may be used. In either case, as with several other projects in this book, a switch to cut it in and out of use when required is a distinct advantage; a D.P.D.T. (double pole, double throw) switch is required to do this, the manner in which it should be connected is shown in Fig. 4.4. Note the use of screened leads to keep hum pickup to a minimum.

With the construction complete, check the board against the circuit diagram, and if all appears well connect the guitar and amplifier and apply power. With R4 at minimum, the sound should come through unchanged; as R4 is increased a striking high frequency boost effect should result. If the unit doesn't work, first check the d.c. conditions; with 9V supply the emitter of TR1 should be at 3.9V, and the collector of TR2 around 3 to 4V. The 'wet finger' test can be applied to this unit; a finger applied to the input should produce a loud hum which can be listened for with a pair of medium or high impedance headphones, or an amplifier. It can be checked for at TR1 emitter and TR2 collector. If

Figure 4.2
Treble booster assembled on board

18

you're using a powerful amplifier make sure you turn the volume down before doing this, or damage to the loudspeakers may result; also take reasonable care if mains-powered equipment is involved.

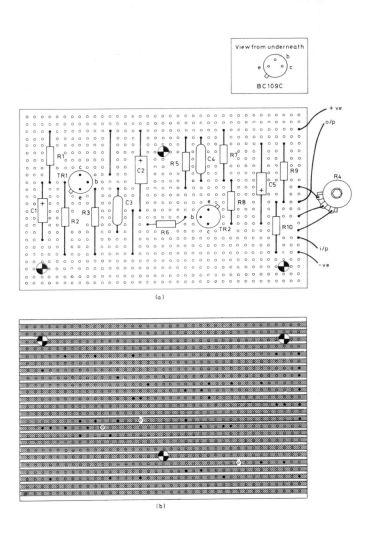

Figure 4.3

Treble boost board (a) Component layout (b) Copper side

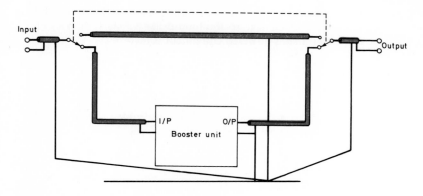

Figure 4.4

Method of connecting switch to cut out boost effect. Note use of screened leads. Screens should be earthed at a common point where possible; this avoids hum pickup which often develops in earth loops

Components list for the treble booster

Resistors
R1   220kΩ
R2   220kΩ
R3   5.6kΩ
R4   47kΩ linear pot
R5   18kΩ
R6   1MΩ
R7   1kΩ
R8   3.9kΩ
R9   3.3kΩ
R10   1kΩ

Capacitors
C1   1μF, 10V
C2   100μF, 10V
C3   0.01μF, polyester
C4   0.01μF, polyester
C5   10μF, 10V

Semiconductors
TR1   BC109C
TR2   BC109C

Miscellaneous
Matrix board 0.1in pitch, 24 strips by 37 holes, case switches as required; jack plug and socket

5

Bass Booster

This project is similar to the treble booster, but the filter network has been rearranged to give a lift to the lower frequencies of the guitar spectrum instead of the top. Increasing the 'boost' by means of the single control gives the instrument a richer, rounded, mellow sound. It will probably be found more effective when used with bass guitars than with the lead guitar for which the last project was designed.

Circuit action

The circuit appears in Fig. 5.1. As with the treble booster, TR1 is used as an emitter follower to buffer the input from the guitar pickup,

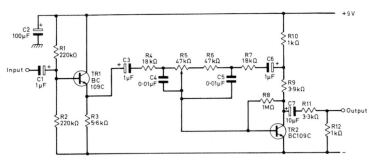

Figure 5.1

Circuit of bass booster

providing a low impedance signal source for the circuitry which follows. The placing of the two 0.01µF capacitors in the treble booster allowed them to double as d.c. blocking capacitors between TR1 emitter and the collector and base of TR2; in this circuit unfortunately it does not, so C3 and C6 have been added to perform this function.

To clarify the action of the circuit it has been redrawn in simplified form in Fig. 5.2 (a), omitting C3, C6 and R6, which were added to tailor the response more precisely to design requirements. It will readily be seen from this that when the wiper of R5 is at either end of its travel it effectively short-circuits one of the two small capacitors, producing

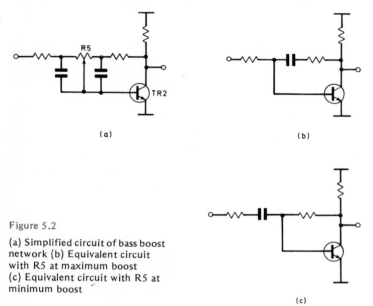

(a)

(b)

Figure 5.2

(a) Simplified circuit of bass boost network (b) Equivalent circuit with R5 at maximum boost (c) Equivalent circuit with R5 at minimum boost

(c)

the circuits of Figs. 5.2 (b) and (c). In the former, the signal reaches the base of the transistor through a pure resistance, but the negative feedback is applied through a small capacitor, effectively reducing the gain of the stage only at higher frequencies. The apparent result is a bass boost, since the low frequencies receive greater amplification than the higher ones. In Fig 5.2 (c), with R5 wiper at the minimum boost end of its travel, the input signal has to pass through the small capacitor before reaching the transistor base; this causes some attenuation of the bass content, whilst the negative feedback is applied through a resistance and so is constant at all frequencies. This would in fact result in some bass cut, but in the full circuit of Fig. 5.1 it will be seen that R6 has been added to prevent this — the value of this resistor has been chosen to make the overall frequency response flat at the minimum setting of R5. Thus R5 controls the response from flat to several dB of boost for lower frequencies.

22

Like the treble booster the circuit exhibits a small amount of overall gain, which is cancelled out by the attenuator formed by R11 and R12 so that the unit may be switched in or out without having to alter the overall volume setting. These resistors may be omitted if desired and the output taken straight from C7.

Construction

Construction of this project is similar to that of the treble booster, using the same size of board and a rather similar component layout (Figs. 5.3 and 5.4), though there are a few extra components on this version. Operation can be from a PP3 battery as the current drain of the circuit is small. After construction and checking, the voltages at TR1 emitter and TR2 collector may be checked, these should be respectively 3.9V and around 3 to 4V. If all appears satisfactory the unit may be connected to an amplifier and tested in the same manner as the treble booster project.

The completed board may be either incorporated into an existing amplifier — perhaps with a separate input for the bass or rhythm player's instrument — or it may be built as a separate self-powered unit. A DPDT switch for cutting it in and out of circuit would be an advantage, as with the treble booster project. Previous notes regarding the use of screened lead for signal connections all apply to this project.

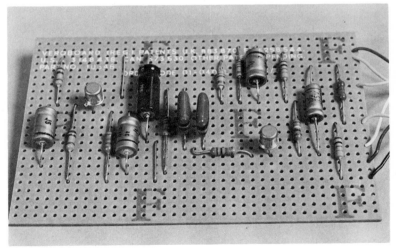

Figure 5.3
Photograph of board

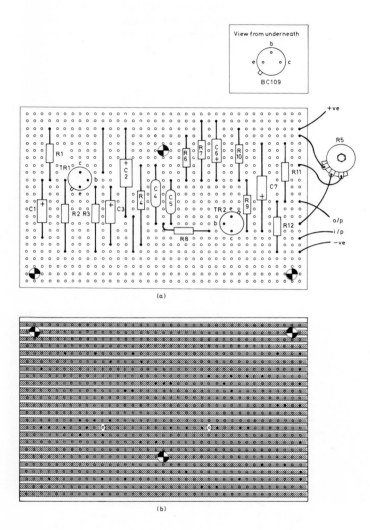

Figure 5.4

Bass booster board (a) Component layout (b) Copper side

Components list for the bass booster

Resistors

R1	220kΩ
R2	220kΩ
R3	5.6kΩ
R4	18kΩ
R5	47kΩ linear pot
R6	47kΩ
R7	18kΩ
R8	1MΩ
R9	3.9kΩ
R10	1kΩ
R11	3.3kΩ
R12	1kΩ

Capacitors

C1	1μF, 10V
C2	100μF, 10V
C3	1μF, 10V
C4	0.01μF, polyester
C5	0.01μF, polyester
C6	1μF, 10V
C7	10μF, 10V

Semiconductors

TR1	BC109C
TR2	BC109C

Miscellaneous
Matrix board, 0.1in pitch, 24 strips by 37 holes
Case, plug and socket, switches etc. as required

6

Fuzz

The sound of Fuzz these days is too well known to need any description, almost every other Pop record released seems to use the effect to some degree. Technically it has been described as the 'ultimate in distortion', and this may indeed be the way in which it was first discovered, when some experimenting guitarist pushed an unfortunate amplifier into providing a volume level way above that which its makers intended.

Circuit action

The process of creating the fuzz sound can be described quite simply; the signal from the guitar is passed through some form of limiting amplifier, which has the effect of 'squaring' it up. Fig. 6.1 shows the effect of such an amplifier on a pure sine wave. (a) shows the undistorted input signal; (b) shows the effect of just a little distortion, with the tops of the sine wave being flattened off a shade, and (c) shows the effect at maximum, where the signal is converted almost to a full square wave. Mathematically it can be shown that a square wave consists of the fundamental frequency plus all its odd harmonics up to infinity; it is these harmonics which produce the typical hard, spiky fuzz sound. Of course the output from a guitar is far from being a pure sine wave — it is already rich in harmonics, so the overall effect of playing through a fuzz amplifier is even more enhanced.

Though the theory of creating fuzz is relatively simple, it is surprisingly difficult to design a reliable fuzz producing circuit. The problem is to create a circuit which can be pushed into distortion in a controlled, predictable manner, without producing any odd parasitic noises of its own or causing a large change in output volume as it does so. In addition, a very high gain is generally necessary to raise the input signal from the guitar to the level required by the distortion producing part of the circuit, and this tends to raise problems of noise and stability.

Figure 6.1

Waveforms at output of fuzz
unit

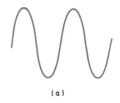

(a)

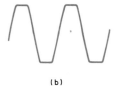

(b)

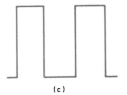

(c)

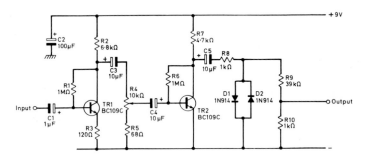

Figure 6.2

Fuzz effect circuit

In Fig. 6.2, TR1 acts as a buffer and amplifier for the guitar signal input. The signal at the collector is amplified by a factor of about 50, but it is still undistorted. R4 acts in the same way as a volume control; from it the signal passes to TR2 for further amplification. This transistor has its emitter taken straight to ground to provide the maximum possible gain. From TR2 collector the signal passes through a current limiting resistor, R8, to the output. Across the output is placed a pair of silicon diodes wired back to back, to pass current in either direction. A silicon diode will not conduct until a forward voltage of approximately 0.6V is present across it. Thus signals below 1.2V peak to peak (0.6V in either direction) are unaffected by the diodes. As the signals rise above this however, the diodes begin to clip the peaks off the waveform, producing the fuzz sound. They also have the effect of clamping the maximum output level to around 1.2V peak to peak, or around 0.85V r.m.s. As the drive to TR2 is increased, either by increasing the input signal or by turning up the control R4, a point is soon reached where this transistor instead of amplifying in the usual sense, is in effect switched completely on and off between supply voltage and zero. This condition is known as clipping and is normally avoided like the plague, but in a fuzz generator it is an advantage, since it can produce an even harsher sound.

As previously stated the output is around 1.2V peak to peak (0.85V r.m.s.) which is far too high if the effect is to be switched in and out with no overall change in volume, so the attenuator formed by R9 and R10 is used to reduce it. If some gain is required the value of R9 can be reduced.

Figure 6.3
Layout of fuzz board

28

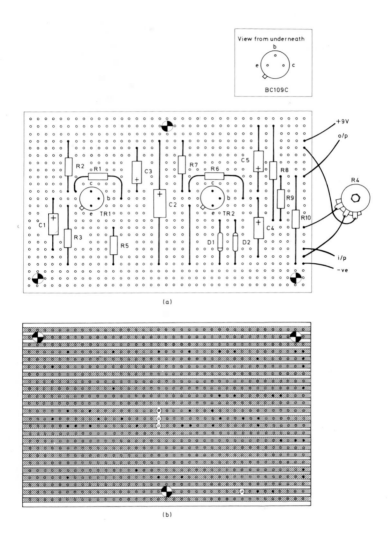

Figure 6.4
Fuzz effect board (c) Component layout (b) Copper side

Construction

Construction, on a piece of 0.1in pitch board, is again straightforward (Figs. 6.3 and 6.4). Only three breaks are required in the strips. The diodes are physically very small, and care should be taken to see they are fitted 'back to back'. Their positive ends are marked, usually with a black band, though it may be some other colour. The current consumption of this project is small, so it may be powered from a PP3 battery. It may be fitted in a case with input and output jacks, or it might be fitted in a foot pedal, with R4 controlled by the pedal. A switch should be provided for switching the effect in and out — this could be a foot switch. A DPDT switch is required for this and should be wired in the same manner as shown for the treble booster project.

Component list for the fuzz unit

Resistors
R1	1MΩ
R2	6.8kΩ
R3	120Ω
R4	10kΩ log. pot.
R5	68Ω
R6	1MΩ
R7	4.7kΩ
R8	1kΩ
R9	39kΩ
R10	1kΩ

Capacitors
C1	1μF, 10V
C2	100μF, 10V
C3	10μF, 10V
C4	10μF, 10V
C5	10μF, 10V

Semiconductors
TR1	BC109C
TR2	BC109C
D1	1N914
D2	1N914

Miscellaneous
Matrix board, 0.1in pitch, 24 strips by 37 holes
Case, switches, plug and socket etc. as required

Troubleshooting should present no problems; if the project does not operate a recheck of the construction against the circuit diagram should be followed by a check of the voltage at the two collectors; both should be around 3V, though this will vary slightly with the gain of the individual transistors used. Applying a finger to either base should produce a loud hum at the output (keep R4 turned up when trying this on TR2).

Using the fuzz unit

Fuzz is generally used on single note runs, where it can provide a very effective sound. It should generally be avoided when playing chords, since the harmonics generated may not necessarily be related musically in the same way as the fundamental notes of the chord, and some very unpleasant noises may result! R4 will control the effect from just a slight 'edge' to the sound to a full, harsh fuzz. The clamping effect of the diodes means that a more or less constant output is maintained over a range of input levels, giving the unit a 'sustain' effect. This is normal with most fuzz units.

7

Simple Mixer

This project introduces a new component to this book, the integrated circuit. Mixer circuits are generally more complex than the one to be described here, incorporating built-in preamps, master tone and volume controls etc., but the purpose remains the same, to combine a number of signals of various levels from different sources into a single output; without allowing them direct contact with each other since they may be of different impedances. The simple circuit of this chapter achieves the basic mixer function with only one active component and has adequate performance for most purposes, it may be employed to combine inputs from several guitars, or guitar and microphone, etc.

The circuit

Before discussing the main circuit a description of the action of the integrated circuit used may be helpful. This is a 741 op-amp. The op-amp (short for operational amplifier) was originally developed for analogue computer use, but it has since become widely available at very low cost and has found application in just about every branch of electronics. There are other varieties of them, offering more specialised characteristics, but the 741 is now probably the most versatile and widely used member of the op-amp family. Its use is simplicity itself; once a few basics have been grasped it is often far simpler to design a circuit using one than a similar circuit using discrete transistor techniques.

The 741 contains a very high gain differential amplifier, the open-loop (without feedback) gain of which is typically around 300 000, or 110dB. It has a single output, but two inputs, referred to as 'inverting' and 'non-inverting', and labelled '−' and '+' respectively on circuit diagrams. If the non-inverting input is positive of the inverting input the output will swing positive, and if it is negative of it the reverse applies. By connecting the output back to the inverting input negative feedback can be applied, and with just two resistors an amplifier of any required gain may be achieved. Fig. 7.1 shows in simplified form how this is done. The non-inverting input is connected directly to ground and a feedback resistor R2 connects the output back to the inverting input.

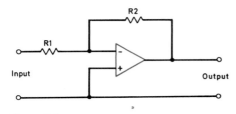

Figure 7.1

Op-amp inverting amplifier circuit

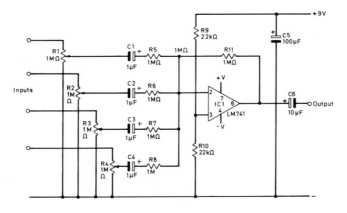

Figure 7.2

Simple mixer circuit

Thus the non-inverting input is held at ground potential, and the inverting input must have the same potential, as any discrepancy will cause the output to swing in the opposite direction, taking the inverting input with it via R2 until input balance is restored. (Assume for the moment that input and output voltages are free to swing both above and below ground potential.) If a voltage is applied to R1, a current will flow through it to the inverting input, and the output will change until an equal and opposite current flows through R2 to cancel it and keep the input at zero volts. If R1 is small in value compared with R2, the output voltage swing will clearly have to be large to counter a small change in voltage applied to R1, hence the device will amplify, with a voltage gain of R2/R1. Since the output swings in the opposite direction to the applied input this arrangement is called an 'inverting amplifier', and as the input is always within a few millivolts of earth potential it is known as a 'virtual earth' input. This property makes it useful for the design of a mixer, as a number of inputs may be fed into it without any form of interaction between them, each input effectively seeing a fixed impedance to earth.

Op-amps are supposed to be used with separate positive and negative supply voltages, above and below earth potential, so where a single battery is used the inputs and output should operate at about half supply voltage. In the circuit of Fig. 7.2 the supply is split by R9 and R10 and applied to the non-inverting input. D.C. negative feedback through R11 causes the inverting input and the output to stabilise at the same voltage, and the blocking capacitors at inputs and output keep this voltage from appearing at signal inputs and output. Since R11 has the same value as the four input resistors, the gain of each channel is unity — it mixes without amplifying. The four pots permit signals of various levels to be adjusted relatively to each other as required.

Construction

This project is assembled on the smaller size of board (Fig. 7.3), ten strips of twenty four holes apiece, and is therefore fairly compact. The cuts (Fig. 7.4) should be made in the strips first, then the links fitted. Note that the three links behind R5 and R8 involve pushing two wires through the same holes in two cases; if no wire thin enough is available to the constructor a strand pulled from a length of flex should suffice. The four input capacitors are tantalum types, partly for their small physical size and partly because their low leakage characteristics prevent any problems arising from d.c. leakage into the amplifier input. Take care they are fitted correctly with respect to polarity. The pot is drawn for clarity with a wire going to the earth terminal from battery negative — in fact connections to the controls should be made in screened lead with the screens connected together at the earth point on the board. The power requirement is of the order of 1.5mA at 9V, so a PP3 battery may be used, though supply voltage is not at all critical, anything from 6 to 30V is quite suitable.

Testing is simple — a voltmeter should show half the supply voltage at the output (pin 6) of the op-amp. If it does not then there is either a faulty component or an error in the construction. Check in particular that there are no blobs of solder bridging the strips, as this is a fairly compactly laid out board. The 741 op-amp is a very robust device and

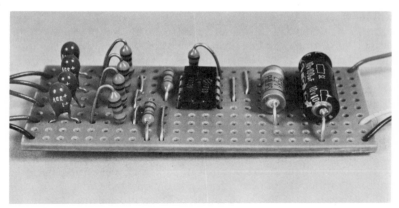

Figure 7.3
Photograph of board

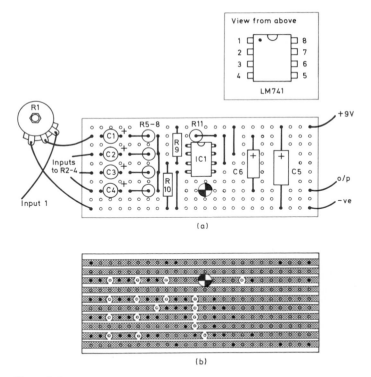

(a)

(b)

Figure 7.4
Mixer board (c) Component layout (b) Copper side

35

will stand an incredible amount of misuse or overload without sustaining damage. If it does fail it generally does so in an obvious manner — the output locks up to within 1V or so of one of the supply rails and stays there. If all appears correct the project is ready to connect up to an amplifier for testing with an input signal.

Using the mixer

This simple unit can be used in a number of ways. It can be simply fitted into an existing amplifier to provide it with multi-input facilities, or it may have one of the preamps of earlier chapters fitted ahead of one or more inputs to permit, say, microphone and guitar to be used simultaneously with the same amplifier. This project offers plenty of scope for tailoring by the individual constructor to suit his needs; even the number of inputs is purely nominal, any number may be added as desired.

Components list for the simple mixer

Resistors
R1	1MΩ log pot
R2	1MΩ log pot
R3	1MΩ log pot
R4	1MΩ log pot
R5	1MΩ
R6	1MΩ
R7	1MΩ
R8	1MΩ
R9	22kΩ
R10	22kΩ
R11	1MΩ

Capacitors
C1	1μF tantalum bead
C2	1μF tantalum bead
C3	1μF tantalum bead
C4	1μF tantalum bead
C5	100μF, 10V electrolytic
C6	10μF, 10V electrolytic

Semiconductor
LC1	LM741 op-amp, 8-pin DIL package

Miscellaneous
Matrix board 0.1in pitch, 10 strips by 24 holes

8

Electronic Pitch Pipes

This simple unit makes use of another i.c., the 555 timer chip, to provide a cheap and effective alternative to the tuning fork or pitch pipes as an aid for tuning guitars and other instruments. Unlike these former gadgets, it does not have to be blown or struck continuously to produce results, and it leaves both the musician's hands free to tune his instrument.

The circuit

The 555 timer chip is now widely available at low cost on the amateur electronics market. It is an extremely versatile device and new uses are continually being found for it — it probably has nearly as many applications as the ubiquitous 741. It was employed in this circuit for its accuracy; it is obviously essential that the frequency of a tuning device shall not drift, and other circuits tried all either exhibited too much drift to be acceptable, or required complex and expensive stabilisation. As a measure of the stability of this little circuit, two tests applied to the prototype were to reduce the battery supply right down to just 3V (way below the manufacturers' minimum specification) and literally to produce frost on the chip itself and the timing capacitor C2 using an aerosol freezer spray. In neither case was there an audible change in the output frequency!

An additional reason for using the 555 was its output stage. Most of the circuits tried required a separate output amplifier of some description, again increasing the circuit cost and complexity, but the 555's 200mA output ability makes it more than capable of driving a small loudspeaker at adequate volume with no additional circuitry at all.

It is not proposed to go into the workings of the chip itself in this book, as it is a fairly complex device internally, comprising two comparators linked to a resistor voltage dividing chain, an RS flip-flop, a couple of transistors and a power output stage.

Fig. 8.1 shows it in the configuration generally used to make an astable multivibrator, producing a near square wave output. Near, because it works by charging and discharging C2. Charging takes place through R1 and R2 plus one of the pre-sets, discharging through R2

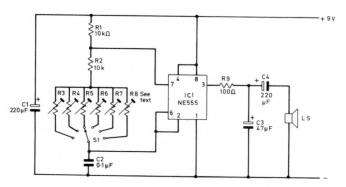

Figure 8.1

Electronic pitch pipes circuit diagram

and the preset only. Thus the charging time is longer than the discharge and the output waveform is slightly asymmetrical. By keeping R1 small this effect is kept to a minimum and is not of any consequence in this circuit. The values of resistors R3 and R8 and capacitor C2 set the frequency, so by making the resistors pre-sets the device may be tuned to produce a range of frequencies; in this case the EADGBE required to set up a guitar, though other tunings may be set if required. The output, being a square wave, is full of harmonics, which makes it a little difficult to tune to in practice, so R9 and C3 are used to filter out a lot of these. C4 blocks d.c. flow through the loudspeaker, which would otherwise cause excessive battery drain and might damage the chip.

Construction

The commonest component on this board is the link (Fig. 8.2), and there are 12 of them. There are also 13 breaks required in the copper strips. The constructor is recommended to start by making the breaks in the strips, since most of these have solder joints right next to them and the cutting becomes more difficult to do once these are made.

Then the links should be fitted, followed by the resistors, capacitors, the i.c., and the pre-sets, in that order for ease of assembly. With the board checked against the circuit diagram the unit may be assembled into a small case together with the loudspeaker, and the switch can be

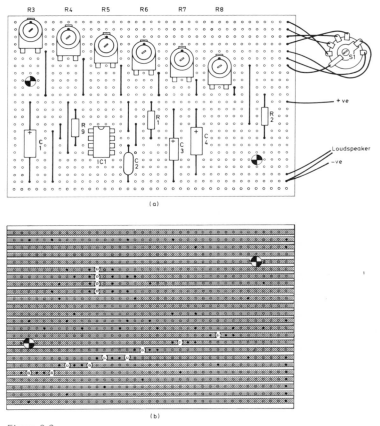

Figure 8.2

Pitch pipes board (a) Component layout (b) Copper side

wired up. A six-way single-pole rotary switch is required. A small slider switch could be used for the on-off function, and since power consumption is around 20mA a PP3 will be sufficient. If the assembly is correct the unit should work first time — there is little to go wrong. If it does not operate, a recheck of the construction followed by a physical check of each component is the only answer; if everything seems correct then the i.c. should be checked by substitution. The 555 is a robust device, however, and seldom causes problems.

Since the pre-sets are arranged in a ramp it is convenient to tune them in this order, though they can in fact be tuned in any sequence. An insulated screwdriver should be used for the tuning as contact between the pre-set wipers and the constructors' fingers may result in hum modulation of the output, making tuning difficult. The notes should be set against a known accurate source.

Use of the pitch pipes

The six notes may be set up to give any required note sequence. To make the design as flexible as possible the component list specifies 100kΩ for all six pre-sets; however a glance at Fig. 8.3 shows that the prototype, set for tuning a standard classical guitar, has the top three

Figure 8.3

Photograph of pitch pipe board

set well below half travel. Though this caused no problems, it might be a good idea if constructors wishing to use it for this purpose used 47kΩ components for R4 and R5, and a 22kΩ for R3. This would undoubtedly make the tuning even simpler and more stable. A final note concerns the loudspeaker, which is in no way critical; speakers of 8 to 35Ω were tried on the prototype with equally satisfactory results. Any duff transistor radio, therefore, might be expected to yield a speaker suitable for this project, providing its d.c. resistance is 8Ω or greater.

Components list for the electronic pitch pipes

Resistors
R1   10kΩ
R2   10kΩ
R3—8   100kΩ preset, miniature horizontal (see text)
R9   100

Capacitors
C1   220μF, 10V
C2   0.1μF, polyester
C3   47μF, 10V
C4   220μF, 10V

Semiconductors
IC1   NE555 timer, 8-pin DIL package

Miscellaneous
Matrix board 0.1in pitch, 24 strips by 37 holes
Loudspeaker, miniature 8Ω (see text)
Switch, single pole 6-way rotary
Slide switch
Case, etc.

9

Waa-Waa

Here's another op-amp based project, this time using the device as a
filter. The waa-waa effect is very popular with guitarists and many
different circuits have been designed to produce it; the one devised for
this project is simple, inexpensive to construct, and provides
performance equal to the best.

The circuit

The effect is generated by sweeping a bandpass filter across the
frequency range of the guitar — from about 40Hz to 6kHz. Most of the

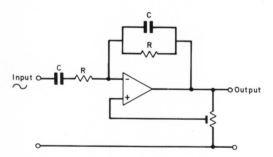

Figure 9.1

Basic bandpass filter circuit

notes comprising the input signal pass through the circuit and emerge at
the output unchanged, but as the centre frequency of the filter is swept
through its spectrum those frequencies close to it get a lift of a few dB
of gain, and this gives rise to the typical waa-waa sound.

The filter is based around a frequency dependent network known as the Wien bridge, which exhibits a phase shift of zero at just one particular frequency. Fig. 9.1 shows in simplified form how this network is used to create a bandpass filter. The Wien Bridge is composed of the two equal value capacitors C and resistors R. The op-amp is connected so that some negative feedback through the bridge is present at all frequencies, but phase relationships within the circuit ensure that this is at a minimum at one particular frequency, so that the gain is highest at this point. Positive feedback is used to bring the circuit close to the point of oscillation and so sharpen up the response, this being applied through the pre-set pot. It will be apparent that the circuit must be driven by a low impedance source, since the source impedance appears in series with the series arm of the bridge, and if high enough would affect the balance of the circuit. The frequency of operation can be found from the simple formula

$$ f = \frac{1}{2\pi R C} $$

where f is in hertz, R in ohms, and C in farads (the farad is a value frequently met in calculations, it is equal to $10^6\mu F$, or one million microfarads). If the two resistors R are made variable using a ganged pot, the operating frequency may be varied at will.

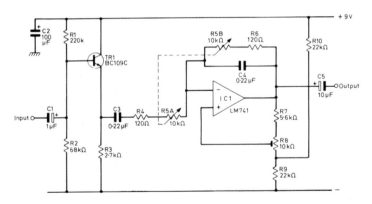

Figure 9.2

Waa-waa circuit diagram

In the full circuit of Fig. 9.2, the op-amp is again working from a single supply, so the voltage is split by R9 and R10 to provide its working point. Pre-set R8 is the positive feedback adjustment and R5 A and B are a ganged pot used to vary the frequency. TR1 is an emitter

43

follower used to buffer the guitar pickup and provide the low-impedance source required by the filter.

Construction

The main circuit assembly is built (Fig. 9.3) on a piece of 0.1in pitch matrix board, with 24 strips of 37 holes. The layout is straightforward and should present no problems, though a check against the circuit diagram is, as usual, advisable after construction. The control pot is a dual-ganged log type available from most electronic suppliers (it is commonly used as a volume control in stereo amplifiers). Power supply

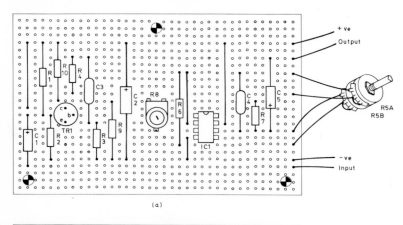

(a)

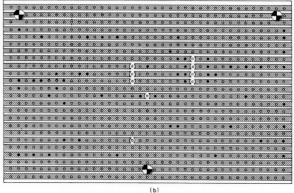

(b)

Figure 9.3

Waa-waa board (a) Component side (b) Copper side

Figure 9.4

Photograph of waa-waa circuit board

requirements are again small; a PP3 battery will provide many hours of operation.

Testing and setting up are reasonably simple — the unit should be connected to an amplifier and the power supply switched on. It will be found that if R8 is turned anti-clockwise the circuit will go into oscillation, producing a continuous loud noise; when this happens slowly turn R8 back until the noise just ceases. Then the guitar should be connected and the best setting for R8 found by trial and error, it will be somewhere just below the point of oscillation. If the unit fails to operate, a couple of voltage checks may help to localise the trouble; providing the supply is at 9V, the emitter voltage of TR1 should be 1.5V, and of course the output (pin 6) of the op-amp should be somewhere near half supply volts.

Waa-waa is almost invariably a foot-controlled effect, the circuitry generally being mounted within the pedal assembly itself, with a drive from the pedal to the pot. Most amateur designs employ a little ingenuity with some 'Meccano' gears to achieve this. A DPDT switch is required to switch the effect in and out as required; this may be foot operated.

Using the waa-waa

Providing the setting-up has been carried out correctly, this unit will produce a very effective sound equal to many of the best commercial units, at a fraction of the cost, and it should prove most useful to the guitarist.

Components list for the waa-waa

Resistors

R1	220kΩ
R2	68kΩ
R3	2.7kΩ
R4	120Ω
R5	10kΩ log dual ganged pot
R6	120Ω
R7	5.6kΩ
R8	10kΩ preset, subminiature horizontal
R9	22kΩ
R10	22kΩ

Capacitors

C1	1μF, 10V
C2	100μF, 10V
C3	0.22μF, polyester
C4	0.22μF, polyester
C5	10μF, 10V

Semiconductors

TR1	BC109C
IC1	LM741 op-amp, 8-pin DIL package

Miscellaneous
Matrix board, 0.1in pitch, 24 strips by 37 holes
D.P.D.T. switch, case, etc. see text

10

Tremolo Generator

This is another project for the guitarist, though it may also be found useful as an additional effect for organs and synthesisers. Tremolo is the name given to rapid modulation of the volume of a sound, though it is sometimes confused with vibrato, which is a small and rapid variation in frequency. The unit to be described here has been designed to produce an exceptionally wide range of control over both the frequency and depth of modulation, enabling the creation of some truly extraordinary and widely differing effects, and it is highly recommended to the player seeking new and fascinating sounds.

Circuit action

The op-amp in this circuit is connected as an astable multivibrator, the action of which can more easily be understood from the simplified circuit of Fig. 10.1. If the output of the op-amp is at positive supply potential, the positive feedback resistor R5 will hold the voltage at the non-inverting input slightly above half supply. If the potential at the inverting input is below this the output will stay positive and C2 will commence charging through R4. When the potential across C2 (and on the inverting input) rises above that on the non-inverting input, the output will start to change state, swinging towards the negative supply rail. Positive feedback through R5 ensures that this swing is very rapid, so the op-amp takes up a new state with the output low, the non-inverting input slightly below half supply, and C2 starts to discharge through R4. When it falls below the potential on the non-inverting the input will suddenly swing back up and the whole cycle will repeat. Thus the circuit is an oscillator, with a symmetrical square-wave output. The frequency is governed primarily by the values of C2 and R4, though variation of the value of R5 will also affect it, since it sets the difference between the two voltages across C2 at which the switching action takes place. If this difference is kept reasonably small, the waveform appearing across C2 will be a reasonable approximation of a triangle wave, which is the waveform required in this project for ramping the signal volume up and down.

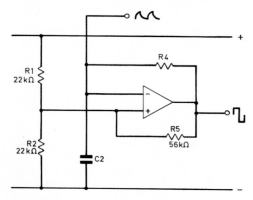

Figure 10.1

Simplified oscillator circuit

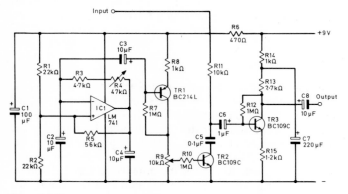

Figure 10.2

Tremolo generator circuit

Turning to the full circuit diagram (Fig. 10.2) the signal from the oscillator stage is taken from C2 and is amplified by TR1 to make the signal amplitude peak to peak approximately equal to the supply voltage. This appears across R9, so the voltage across this pot can be considered as ramping smoothly up and down between zero and almost full supply voltage.

48

Transistor TR2 is used in conjunction with R11 as an attenuator stage. There are several methods of achieving electronic attenuation; most circuits of this type employ an FET as a voltage controlled resistor, but the transistor attenuator used here is simpler, and the performance was found to be excellent with input signals of up to about 100mV, well above the average guitar pickup output. The amount of signal which TR2 can conduct to ground depends upon the base current fed to it by R10; this in turn depends upon the voltage on the wiper of R9, so the attenuation variation rate is set by the oscillator frequency, and the amount of attenuation can be adjusted by means of R9, the 'depth' control.

C5 keeps the low frequency signal from the oscillator from appearing at the output. Since the effect is generated by attenuation of the input signal, TR3 is used to boost the average output level back enough to make up the loss. C7 decouples the collector supply to TR3 to ensure that low frequency variations in the supply voltage caused by the oscillator do not reach the output.

A difficulty encountered in the design of this project was a loud ticking on the output, which appeared after the finished board was constructed, and appeared to be due to capacitive coupling between IC1 output and components around TR3. After some experiment, it appeared that the best way to overcome this problem was the inclusion of C4 between the op-amp output and ground. This not only has the effect of shorting the high frequency voltage spikes that produced the clicks to ground, it also causes the amplifiers' internal overload protection to operate momentarily at each switch-over, slowing the rate at which the output can change state. Although the overload protection was not designed for this, extended testing has shown that it does no harm, and this modification does totally cure the problem of the ticks, far better than a number of technically more elegant solutions tried. It did produce a slight 'thump' through the supply rail, but the inclusion of separate decoupling components R6 and C1 cured this.

Construction

Construction of this project is straightforward, providing the usual sequence of component fitting and checking of the assembled board is followed. Note that 13 breaks are required in the copper strips (Fig. 10.3). R4, which controls the rate, is wired so that clockwise rotation reduces the rate rather than increasing it; this is done in order to use the log characteristic of the pot to best effect. A linear pot could be used instead, but would not give such a smooth control. As with a number of the previous projects the unit may be cased separately or it may be mounted inside an existing amplifier. Switching to cut the effect in and

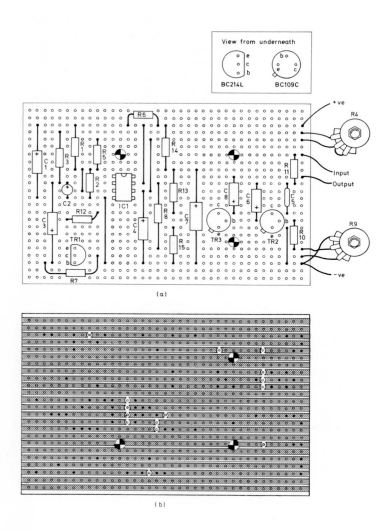

Figure 10.3

Tremolo generator board (a) Component layout (b) Copper side

Figure 10.4

Photograph of tremolo generator board

out would be an advantage, though not absolutely essential since with R9 turned right down it has no effect. The power requirement is again small enough to permit the use of a PP3 battery.

In the event of the project failing to operate the following tests may prove helpful. If R4 is turned to minimum resistance, (anticlockwise) a voltmeter connected across C4 (10V range) will read the average output voltage of the op-amp, which should be a little less than half the supply voltage. Turning R4 fully clockwise will slow the oscillator speed sufficiently for some oscillation to be apparent on the meter needle. If these tests are not correct, re-check the wiring around IC1, noting particularly if the capacitors C2, C3 and C4 are fitted correctly with respect to polarity. Similarly the voltage across the depth pot R9 may be checked, and the oscillation observed here also. TR3 collector voltage may be checked, it should be around 3 to 5V. There are no voltage checks for TR2, but if TR3 is functioning correctly a finger placed on TR3 base, TR2 base, TR2 collector, C6 negative end and the input lead should all produce loud noises from the amplifier (make sure the volume is turned well down before trying this)!

Using the tremolo generator

The effects this unit is capable of producing almost defy description! The amount of alteration in the volume may be varied continuously from none at all to being completely switched on and off, and the rate at which this happens is variable from two or three times a second to around thirty. A little experimentation with the device will soon show what it can do, and in addition to the usual tremolo sound the enthusiast will be able to obtain some really unusual sounds.

Components list for the tremolo generator

Resistors
R1	22kΩ
R2	22kΩ
R3	4.7kΩ
R4	47kΩ log pot
R5	56kΩ
R6	470Ω
R7	1MΩ
R8	1kΩ
R9	10kΩ log pot
R10	1MΩ
R11	10kΩ
R12	1MΩ
R13	2.7kΩ
R14	1kΩ
R15	1.2kΩ

Capacitors
C1	100μF, 10V
C2	10μF, 10V tantalum bead
C3	10μF, 10V
C4	10μF, 10V
C5	0.1μF, polyester
C6	1μF, 10V
C7	220μF, 10V
C8	10μF, 10V

Semiconductors
TR1	BC214L
TR2	BC109C
TR3	BC109C
IC1	LM741 op-amp, 8-pin DIL

Miscellaneous
Matrix board, 0.1in pitch, 24 strips by 37 holes
Case, plug and socket, knobs, switch etc. as required

11

Mini Organ

Miniature electronic organs of the type in this project have become popular in recent years, with at least one very successful commercial version selling well in the shops. They cannot really be classified as serious musical instruments since they are monophonic, i.e. only one note can be played at a time; however they are great fun to play with. The serious student of music may find such an instrument useful for picking out melodies when studying a composition, and children will be delighted for hours with it. The organ in this project has switchable vibrato, which gives a very pleasing tone, and incorporates a novel feature in that the whole keyboard range may be raised or lowered through an entire octave, allowing rapid tuning of the instrument to any basic key. It has a two octave keyboard, with semitones, although it has been designed in such a manner as to make these optional; they may be left out if not required. The output power is around half a watt, quite sufficient to allow good room volume to be obtained with a small loudspeaker.

The circuit

The note generating part of this circuit (Fig. 11.1) is based upon the 741 used as an oscillator, the action of which was described in detail in the last chapter, covering the tremolo generator. IC2 actually generates the notes; C3 is the frequency determining capacitor with a fixed value of $0.1 \mu F$ whilst the resistor is variable, in this case in steps, by the chain of fixed resistors which make up the keyboard. It was stated in the tremolo project circuit description that alteration of the positive feedback resistor would affect the oscillator frequency; here this is used to good effect by the inclusion of the variable resistor VR1. This can be used to alter the frequency without any need for change in the keyboard resistor chain and allows rapid tuning of the instrument to

53

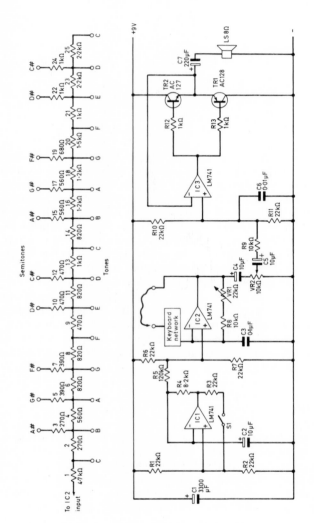

Figure 11.1
Mini organ circuit diagram

54

any key. The values of VR1 and R8 have been chosen to give a total shift of just over an octave in frequency.

A plain tone output soon becomes very boring to listen to, so instruments of this type are generally provided with a simple vibrato circuit. In this circuit IC1 is used as the vibrato generator, and is again a simple 741 astable oscillator, this time running at a frequency of just a few hertz. If the vibrato is not required the positive feedback path is broken by means of switch S1; when this is done the output and inverting input settle rapidly to the half supply voltage provided by R1 and R2 at the non-inverting input. Otherwise the output signal, taken from the inverting input, has an approximately triangular waveform and is applied through R5 to the non-inverting input of IC2. Thus it ramps the voltage on this input slightly, causing a very small, rapid fluctuation of IC2's output frequency. This gives a far more pleasant 'organ-like' tonal quality to the sound produced. The value of R5 controls the vibrato depth; interested experimenters may like to try different values for this resistor to see which suits their taste the best.

From IC2 the signal is taken via C4 and the volume control VR2, through C5 and R9 to the output stage constructed around IC3. R9 sets the maximum volume; constructors building this project for young children might be well advised to increase its value a little, as doing so will both limit the amount of noise produced and reduce the battery consumption. C6 improves the tone a little by filtering out the harsher high frequency harmonics.

IC3 together with transistors TR1 and TR2 forms a crude class B amplifier stage. In a class B amplifier separate transistors are used to handle positive and negative half cycles of the output signal, the advantage being that the current consumed is directly proportional to the signal level, resulting in lower power consumption at settings below full volume. The disadvantage of a class B stage is that non-linearity of transistor gain characteristics for small currents results in distortion of the signal at the point where each transistor switches off and its partner takes over; this is known as 'cross-over' distortion. To overcome this a conventional class B stage is designed to pass a continuous small current through both transistors even under no-signal conditions, known as the 'quiescent' current. This in turn leads to problems of thermal stability, since output transistors working hard tend to get hot, and a hot transistor passes more current than when it is cold.

In the simple circuit of this project there is no ambient current through the output transistors; instead negative feedback through IC3 is used to cancel out the non-linearity. The op-amp needs to see a voltage at its inverting input equal to that applied at the non-inverting, and will adjust the drive to the transistors until it does so. Thus the signal applied to IC3 non-inverting input appears at the coupled emitters of the output pair, at the same voltage, but with sufficient power to drive a loudspeaker. No thermal stabilisation is required because there is no quiescent current flow through the transistors. In practice a very small amount of cross-over distortion remains, but the performance of this amplifier would beat many commercial radio output stages hollow, and for this application a little distortion merely helps to improve the sound anyway!

The current drawn by the output at high volume tends to cause problems if a small battery is used unless a decoupling capacitor of at least $2500\mu F$ is used; to be on the safe side a $3300\mu F$ component is specified for the decoupler C1.

At this point a note about the keyboard resistors will not be amiss. It is of course impossible to obtain precise tuning using fixed resistors, and the accuracy of the intervals does also vary slightly with changes in the setting of VR1. With 5% tolerance resistors, however, a surprisingly accurate tuning is obtainable, quite good enough for an instrument of this type. An alternative approach would be to employ pre-set resistors for the notes and tune each individually; this could easily be done, but would add substantially to both the size and the cost of the project. Most constructors will probably find the fixed resistor arrangement more than sufficient in accuracy.

Construction

This is the most complex project so far covered in this book, so the absolute beginner might be advised to tackle one of the simpler preceding projects to gain some experience before trying his hand at it. This said, the circuit is simple and reliable and should not present any real problems providing reasonable care is taken with the construction.

A piece of 0.1in pitch matrix board (Figs. 11.2 and 11.3) is used as the basis for construction; proceed by first making the cuts in the copper strips. Next fit the links; there are 15 of them. Then follow the usual construction sequence, but leave the end-mounted keyboard resistors and the big decoupling capacitor until last. Check the construction carefully against the drawing, then hook up the controls, loudspeaker, a flexible lead from the 'stylus' connection, and switch on. Touching any of the keyboard strips should produce a tone from the speaker, and if the keyboard resistors are correctly fitted it should be possible to play two scales working up along the strips towards the stylus connection.

If the circuit fails to operate, first check the volume control is not turned to minimum! Then check the voltage at the positive end of C7, which should be at exactly half supply. The voltage at the output (pin 6) of IC1 should read around half supply whether S1 is closed or not, when it is closed a slight fluctuation may be noticed on the voltmeter

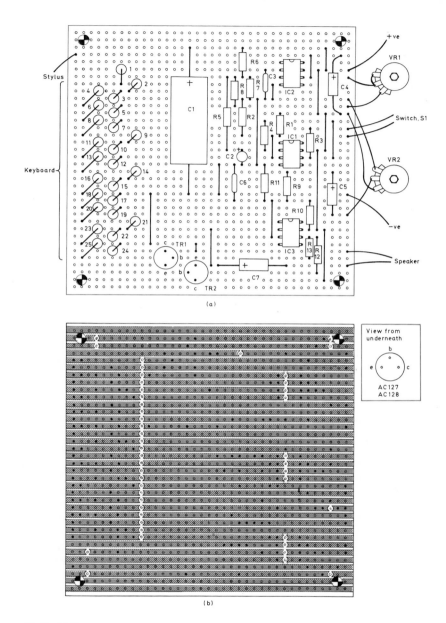

Figure 11.2

Mini organ board (a) Component layout (b) Copper side

Figure 11.3
Photograph of board layout

needle — it is in fact switching rapidly between the supply rails, but the meter will display the average value. IC2 output should be around half supply as long as a note is being played — like IC1 it is in fact switching up and down, but far more rapidly. When the 'stylus' is removed from the keyboard it will stop within a volt or so of one of the supply rails, which one depends upon the charge present on C3 at the instant of stylus removal. A pair of high impedance headphones may be used to check the operation of IC1 and IC2, in both cases apply between ground and pin 6 via a d.c. blocking capacitor of 1μF or so. The note being played should be heard at IC2, whilst IC1 will produce a rapid ticking sound.

The method of boxing up is a matter for the preference of the individual constructor, the only problem being the design of some form of keyboard. A proper keyboard is not really justified on this instrument since only one note at a time can be sounded. The commonest approach is to etch a picture of a keyboard on printed circuit board, along the lines of that shown in Fig. 11.4, and attach a contact probe, possibly made from an old ballpoint pen, to a very flexible lead to form a stylus for picking out the notes. Etching a P.C. board is an interesting process and not at all difficult; kits are available from electronic suppliers for the purpose, or the materials may be bought separately. Copper clad board, both glass fibre and paxolin, is readily available; the wanted areas of copper can be masked by painting with plastic enamel such as that sold for painting plastic scale model kits, and the board etched in ferric chloride solution, which is quite easy to handle. Ferric chloride in crystal form is available from electronics suppliers, or the local chemist may be able to help. The masked board is simply immersed in the solution and stirred occasionally until the process is complete; it usually takes an hour or so, depending upon the temperature. After

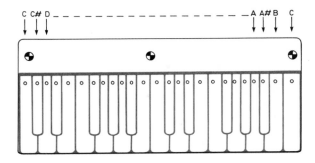

Figure 11.4
Suggested keyboard etching pattern

etching the board should be very thoroughly rinsed under the tap, and the paint cleaned off with wire wool. In the case of the keyboard tinning the copper areas with a soldering iron will improve stylus contact reliability.

Another interesting keyboard possibility is the use of reed switches operated with a small magnet in place of the stylus; by suitably placing the reeds under a moving magnet a musical box might be produced.

This project will operate from a PP3 battery, but full volume output requires some 60mA, so if long periods of playing at high volume are envisaged the constructor should consider the use of a larger battery such as the PP7 or PP9 type.

Using the organ

In use the pitch control VR1 should first be set to give the basic key required, and the vibrato switched in or out as necessary. After a little practice the instrument will be found easy to play and should provide a great deal of pleasure to the user.

Components list for the mini organ

Resistors

R1	22kΩ
R2	22kΩ
R3	22kΩ
R4	8.2kΩ
R5	120kΩ
R6	22kΩ
R7	22kΩ
R8	10kΩ
R9	10kΩ
R10	22kΩ
R11	22kΩ
R12	1kΩ
R13	1kΩ
VR1	22kΩ lin pot
VR2	10kΩ log pot

Capacitors

C1	3300μF, 25V
C2	10μF, tantalum bead
C3	0.1μF, polyester
C4	10μF, 25V
C5	10μF, 25V
C6	0.01μF, polyester
C7	220μF, 10V

Semiconductors

IC1, 2, 3	741 op-amp, 8-pin DIL package
TR1	AC128
TR2	AC127

Miscellaneous

Matrix board 0.1in pitch, 36 strips by 37 holes

S1	SPST min. slide switch
L/S	8Ω min. speaker

Keyboard resistors

1	4.7kΩ	14	820Ω
2	270Ω	15	560Ω
3	270Ω	16	1.2kΩ
4	560Ω	17	560Ω
5	390Ω	18	1.2kΩ
6	820Ω	19	680Ω
7	390Ω	20	1.5kΩ
8	820Ω	21	1kΩ
9	470Ω	22	1kΩ
10	470Ω	23	2.2kΩ
11	820Ω	24	1kΩ
12	470Ω	25	2.2kΩ
13	1kΩ		

12

Electronic Drum

The electronic drum is more of a novelty than a serious instrument except in rhythm generators, where usually several of them are tuned to different pitches and operated in sequence by digital circuitry to produce a most realistic 'backing' sound. The touch operated drum is a fascinating toy for the electronic enthusiast to play with however, and is a real 'finger tapper's' delight, guaranteed to drive anyone nearby nuts!

A number of drum circuits have appeared in the electronics press, but most of them are too simple and the resulting performance has not been very satisfactory. At the expense of a little more complexity the circuit of this project offers excellent performance and complete temperature stability. It is still relatively inexpensive to construct, since the four logic gates in the touch circuit are contained in a single i.c. available at the time of writing for little more than the cost of a single transistor.

The circuit

The full circuit appears in Fig. 12.1, and for simplicity is best described in two sections. The principle of producing the drum sound is to use an oscillator circuit with its feedback adjusted so that it is just below the point of oscillation; hit it (electrically speaking!) and it rings briefly, producing a 'ping' or a 'bonk' depending upon the basic frequency selected. The type of oscillator generally employed in drum circuits is a phase shift circuit constructed around a single transistor, which is not very satisfactory since quite small changes of temperature can alter the gain of the transistor enough to significantly change the length of time for which the circuit rings; it may even cause it to burst into full oscillation. In this project the oscillator is designed around an op-amp, the gain of which is defined by external components and once set up remains virtually constant at any temperature. The circuit is again based upon the Wien bridge used in the waa-waa project, but it is connected in a slightly different manner; the bridge feeds back into the

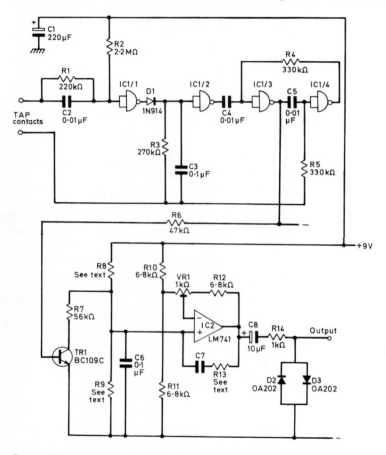

Figure 12.1

Electronic drum circuit diagram

non-inverting input and negative feedback to the inverting input is used to control the gain. The bridge series arm consists of C7 and R13, whilst the parallel arm consists of C6 together with R8 and R9, which also split the supply to provide the d.c. operating point for the op-amp. From the point of view of the bridge R8 and R9 are effectively connected in parallel to ground; as their combined resistance must be equal to the value of R13 they are each twice the value of R13. The value of these three resistors can be selected to give the fundamental frequency — and hence the size of drum — required.

The attenuation of the Wien bridge network is 3, so the amplifier must have a gain of 3 if it is to sustain oscillation. The resistor network of R10, R11 and R12, together with the pre-set VR1 has been arranged to give an adjustable gain of 2.6 to 3.3, making precise adjustment to just below the point of oscillation a simple matter. The output from the op-amp is a pure sine wave. It was found that the introduction of a few harmonics produced a more realistic sound, so D2 and D3 were added to do this by clipping the signal.

So much for the actual 'bonker'; now to the means of 'hitting' it. Many of the published circuits have relied upon simply touching a sensitive point of the circuit and depending upon 'hum' voltage (usually present in the body in buildings with mains wiring due to capacitive coupling) to operate it. This is unsatisfactory in the extreme; there may be insufficient hum, the instant of touching may coincide with the zero crossing point of the hum voltage, and the 'bonk' usually takes place when the finger is removed from the contact, not when it is applied. After trying various input circuits the use of a C-MOS digital chip was decided upon; its very high input impedance makes it ideal for the purpose and the four gates available on the single inexpensive chip make it easy to design an input which delivers a single precisely timed pulse to the 'bonker' each time the input is touched.

The chip chosen is the 4011B which contains four 2-input 'nand' gates. The inputs of each gate are strapped together, turning them into inverters; when the input is 'high' (near +rail voltage) the output is 'low' (near — rail voltage) and vice versa. The input of gate 1 is held high by the 2.2MΩ resistor R2 until shorted to ground by a finger placed across the touch contacts, so the output is low and goes high whenever the input is touched. Under certain conditions the input may respond to hum, causing the output to switch up and down at mains frequency (50Hz) so the output of gate 1 is fed through D1 and R3 and C3, which have a time constant of 40ms, twice the mains hum period, and ensure that the input of gate 2 is held high continuously so long as finger contact is maintained. Thus gate 2 output is normally high and goes low as long as a finger is placed on the touch contact.

Gates 3 and 4 are wired to make a monostable, a circuit which is normally in one state, but switches briefly after an input pulse, giving an output pulse of fixed length. The input of gate 4 is normally held low by R5, so its output and hence the input of gate 3 are high, and gate 3 output is low. A short negative pulse arriving at gate 3 input through C4 (as gate 2 output goes low when the contacts are touched) causes gate 3 to switch, its output goes high, taking gate 4 input high via C5, gate 4 output then goes low and holds gate 3 input low to maintain the circuit in its new state until C5 discharges through R5, when gate 4 input goes low again and the circuit reverts to its former state. The output is thus a short pulse of duration determined by R5 and C5 — in this case about 5ms — every time the contacts are touched.

The short pulse from the monostable is used to switch transistor TR1 on for a brief period, pulling the 'bonker' input low and then sharply releasing it to allow it to ring freely.

Construction

Construction, on a piece of 0.1in pitch Veroboard with 24 strips of 36 holes, presents no difficulties providing the usual construction procedures are followed. Some of the components are placed fairly close together in this project (Fig. 12.2), so it is recommended that the link-resistor-capacitor-semiconductor construction sequence is followed to make assembly as easy as possible. The values of R8, R9 and R13 may be selected from Table 12.1.

Leave the fitting of IC1 till last. The one — and practically only — disadvantage of C-MOS ICs is that their very high input impedance — typically thousands of megohms — means that they are easily damaged by static voltages often present on the body. Note that the chip specified is the 4011B which is fitted with internal diode protection; the earlier A series was not. It should be supplied with its pins pressed into what

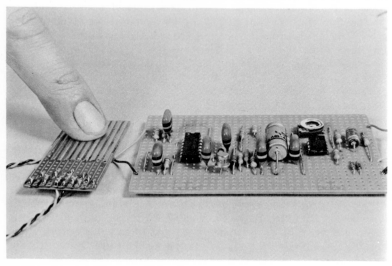

Figure 12.2

Photograph of board layout

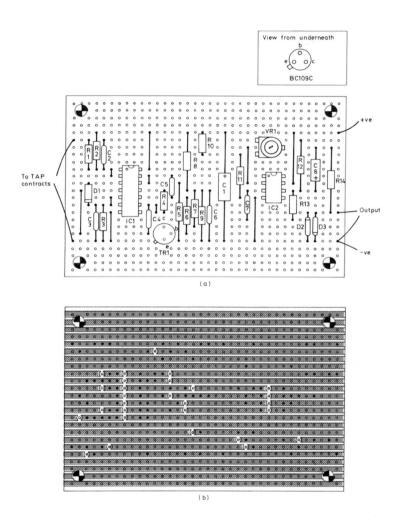

Figure 12.3

Electronic drum circuit board (a) Component layout
(b) Copper side

Table 12.1. Values for R8, R9, R13

Hz	R8, R9	R13	Drum sound
40	68kΩ	39kΩ	Bass drum
70	47kΩ	22kΩ	Low mid range drum
100	27kΩ	15kΩ	Good mid range
150	22kΩ	10kΩ	Good high range
200	15kΩ	8.2kΩ	High, or low bongo drum
300	10kΩ	4.7kΩ	High bongo

looks like a piece of black foam rubber; this is conductive and should be kept in place until the chip is to be fitted. When fitting handle the pins during insertion as little as possible, and solder the earth pin first (pin 7, bottom left) then the + supply pin (pin 14, top right) before the others. This enables the internal protection to operate correctly. Early users of C-MOS used to suggest all kinds of elaborate precautions, such as the constructor being physically earthed to a metal-topped bench during construction! — experience suggests this sort of thing is not strictly necessary, but the constructor might do well to avoid taking a run on a nylon carpet, wearing nylon overalls, or stroking the cat before handling a C-MOS component!

Testing is straightforward; the unit should be connected to an amplifier, the power supply (a PP3 is quite sufficient) connected, and VR1 turned slowly clockwise. If the oscillator circuit is working correctly a loud tone should start to emanate from the loudspeaker; when this happens back off VR1 until it just stops. Touching the bared ends of a pair of wires from the input should now produce a sound varying from a dull thud through something very like a real drum to a sound not unlike a piece of metal being twanged, depending on the setting of VR1. A little experiment will soon find the best operating point. Some voltage checks may help if the unit fails to operate; pin 6 of IC2 should be at half supply, and the operation of IC1 may be checked at the four outputs, pins 3, 4, 10 and 11 respectively, working from the circuit description. If pin 3 shows a voltage around half supply when the contacts are touched it is switching at 50Hz, this is normal.

Using the drum

A drum, and this one is no exception, is a loud, low frequency intrument, so for a realistic sound this project must be used with an amplifier-speaker combination capable of handling such signals. It will not give good results with, say, half a watt into a 4in speaker. One drum on its own would not be much use; the design of this project was carried out with low cost very much in mind so that two or more drums of various frequencies may be built.

If the project is to be used with a battery powered amplifier the input touch contact must be designed so that the touching finger bridges two contacts, connecting the R1—C2 lead to earth; a good way to achieve this is by using a piece of matrixboard with alternate strips connected to earth and input, as shown in Fig. 12.2. The strips can be seen to be tinned with solder; this overcomes the problem of unreliable contact due to oxidation of the copper in the strips. If the unit is to be used with mains powered equipment (earthed chassis, please!) the earth contact may be dispensed with — just touching the R1—C2 input lead on its own will provide reliable operation from the hum pickup. In this case the touch contact can be no more than a small, well insulated metal plate.

Components list for the electronic drum

Resistors

R1	220kΩ
R2	2.2MΩ
R3	270kΩ
R4	330kΩ
R5	330kΩ
R6	47kΩ
R7	56kΩ
R8	see text
R9	see text
R10	6.8kΩ
R11	6.8kΩ
R12	6.8kΩ
R13	see text
R14	1kΩ
VR1	1kΩ horizontal min. pre-set

Capacitors

C1	220μF, 10V
C2	0.01μF, polyester
C3	0.1μF, polyester
C4	0.01μF, polyester
C5	0.01μF, polyester
C6	0.1μF, polyester
C7	0.1μF, polyester
C8	10μF, 10V

Semiconductors

IC1	4011B C-MOS quad 2-input nand
IC2	741 op-amp, 8-pin DIL package
TR1	BC109C
D1	1N914
D2, D3	OA202

Miscellaneous
Matrix board, 0.1in pitch, 24 strips by 36 holes

13

Guitar Practice Amplifier

The design aims for this amplifier were that it should operate directly from a guitar pickup, which has a rather lower output than a radio tuner or record pickup; that it should have a really good clean sound, and that it should have an output in excess of a watt, so that the guitarist may if he wishes use it to entertain his family and friends in the average sized living room. A simple tone control was considered desirable, as was headphone socket to permit private practice sessions without disturbing the rest of the family. An additional advantage was to be operation from a 9V battery to avoid the problems of constructing a mains power supply.

A 'discrete' design was preferred to one constructed around one of the commercially available integrated amplifiers, as these tend to become obsolete quite quickly and the performance of those tried fell short of expectations.

This project is simple to build and set up, has a truly excellent performance and should find many uses for the electronic enthusiast as well as the guitarist.

The circuit

In the circuit of Fig. 13.1, TR1 is used as a preamp to enable the circuit to work directly from the small signal provided by a guitar pickup. If a different overall level of gain is required, the value of R4 may be altered slightly. C3 and R2 decouple the collector supply to TR1 to isolate it from supply voltage fluctuations due to the current demands of the main amplifier. C5 and VR1 form a simple top-cut tone control by shorting high frequencies to ground.

From TR1 collector the signal passes through the volume control VR2 to the main amplifier, the action of which may be better understood by referring to the simplified diagram of Fig. 13.2. The output pair, TR3 and TR4, are of opposite polarity (*pnp* and *npn*) so a signal fed to their bases will tend to turn one off and the other on, depending on signal polarity. They are driven by TR2, with collector load R4, so the voltage at their coupled emitters depends upon the current supplied

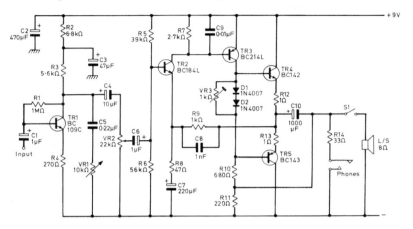

Figure 13.1

Practice amplifier circuit diagram

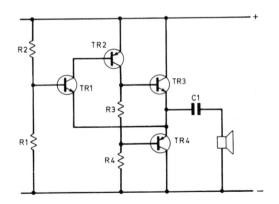

Figure 13.2

Simplified circuit diagram of power amplifier

by TR2. In the quiescent (no signal) state this voltage should be around half supply voltage to permit the greatest possible swing in either direction when a signal is applied. It is fed back to the emitter of TR1, the base of which is fixed at half supply voltage by R1 and R2. If the voltage at TR1 emitter differs from that at its base, it will increase or decrease the bias current to the output driver TR2 until balance is restored. A simple way of following this action is to consider what would happen if the output voltage were, for example lower than the input. TR1 emitter would be lower than its base, so it would pass more current to TR2, tending to turn it on (TR2 is *pnp*) so that it provides more drive current, making the bases of TR3 and TR4 more positive. This would tend to turn on TR3 (*npn*) and turn off TR4 (*pnp*), so the emitter voltage of these two would rise until the balance of the circuit was correct. If the output voltage were too high, of course the reverse would apply. An audio signal applied to the base of TR1 would cause it to drive the following transistors to achieve a corresponding voltage at its emitter; the output taken from the emitters of TR3 and TR4 has enough power to drive a loudspeaker. C1 prevents d.c. current flow through the speaker.

TR3 and TR4 handle positive and negative half cycles of the output signal respectively. To avoid a gap at the cross-over point (which would produce the deadly cross-over distortion) a small current must flow through both transistors in the quiescent state to ensure that they are never both completely turned off. R3, shown in the simplified circuit, would generate a small potential between the bases to achieve this; in practice this current must be temperature stabilised. More will be said about this shortly.

In the circuit of Fig. 13.1, the power amplifier part works exactly like the simple example described, with a few small modifications. Firstly, in addition to current gain some a.c. voltage amplification is required, so the signal fed back to TR2 emitter is attenuated by R8 and R9, causing the output to be driven further to make the signal at TR2 emitter follow that at its base. C7 ensures that there is no attenuation of the feedback at d.c. so the circuit does not drift away from its half supply voltage quiescent point. The voltage supplied to the base of TR2 is a little higher than half supply to allow for the base-emitter junction voltage drop of TR2. C8 and C9 reduce the gain at high frequencies and thus cure any tendency towards r.f. instability, and R7 is added to provide a suitable collector load for TR2. TR3 collector load is returned to the output rather than the negative rail to increase the available voltage swing to drive the output pair at signal frequencies.

The problem of stabilising the output quiescent current has caused many a designer's headache. The basic trouble is that output transistors tend to get hot at high volume levels; as they warm up so the base-emitter voltage falls, and if the base potential difference is held constant the quiescent current increases, in turn generating more heat. If power consumption is to be kept to reasonable levels some means of adjusting the bias voltage to compensate for variations in transistor temperature has to be found. The usual approach is the use of a thermistor

70

(temperature sensitive resistor) but this was rejected for this design as constructors might have difficulty obtaining the right thermistor.

The output transistors used in this project are silicon types, because silicon transistors are much less temperature sensitive than the germanium types more commonly employed, and because they lend themselves readily to diode stabilisation. The bias potential is derived from the forward voltage drop across D1 and D2, two readily available and inexpensive silicon diodes. A rise in temperature causes the potential across these two diodes to fall, so by physically attaching them to the output transistors they can be made to accurately compensate for temperature-induced changes in the transistor base-emitter potentials. The pre-set VR3 is used to set the initial value of quiescent current to the minimum required to prevent distortion, and the stability of this circuit has been found a great improvement over the majority of thermistor stabilised output stages.

Construction

Construction (Fig. 13.3), on a piece of matrix board, 0.1in pitch, with 36 strips of 37 holes, follows conventional practice and should not cause any difficulties (Fig. 13.4). The two output transistors have their leads spaced at 0.1in and may be mounted flush to the board. The heat sinks should be attached before they are fitted, these are push-on types and are simply pressed into place on the TO5 transistor cans. Take care when fitting TR5 to the board that the sink does not touch C2 or any nearby links.

Now for the tricky bit — the wire leads of the two 1N4007 diodes should be bent so that when fitted — note the polarity — they lie between the lobes of the heatsinks (Fig. 13.5). When the leads appear to be correctly bent, apply a little spot of epoxy glue to the sink to hold the fitted diode firmly in place, then solder it into position, and if necessary apply a twist of wire to hold it tight to the sink until the glue has set. Ensure the diode leads do not touch the heat sinks.

After a careful check of the construction the amplifier is ready for testing. Connect the output to an 8Ω speaker, and ensure that the input is connected to a signal source or the volume control is turned right down before connecting the supply, as with an open-circuit input and high volume setting it may drive full output on hum picked up on the input leads. The quiescent drain of this project is about 6 to 7 mA, but at full output it draws over 100mA from the supply, so the constructor is recommended to use a fairly large battery, say a PP9. It is a good idea to connect an ammeter in series with the supply before

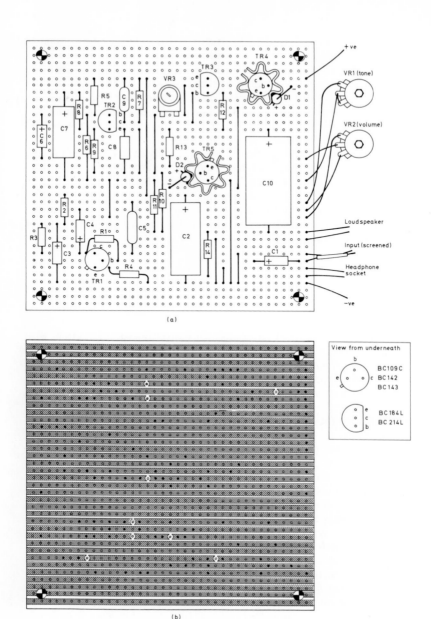

Figure 13.3

Practice amplifier (a) Component layout (b) Copper side

Figure 13.4

Photograph of board layout

first switching on in case a fault is present which could cause a heavy current drain, but don't mistake the switch-on surge of C2 and C10 for a fault. If all appears well, check the voltage at the positive end of C10, which should be within ½V of half the supply voltage. If this is all right apply an input signal and increase the volume a little; there should be plenty of sound from the speaker. If this test is satisfactory, turn the volume right down, turn pre-set VR3 fully anti-clockwise and note the total current drawn by the amplifier, then increase it by 1mA by turning VR3 clockwise. This sets the correct quiescent current. 1mA may sound a little low, but it was found more than sufficient to completely eliminate cross-over distortion on the prototype. The amplifier is now ready for use.

In the event of its not operating correctly the following checks may help. The voltage across C3 should be about 6V, and at TR1 collector about 2.5V. A heavy current consumption may be caused by a fault in the output biasing set-up, D1 and D2 connections should be checked first, or by a faulty output transistor. Another possible cause of this symptom is h.f. oscillation — check C8 and C9. Any other faults in the power stage will normally result in the output driving to one of the supply rails and staying there — a careful check of the state of each transistor (on or off) may help to locate the trouble.

Figure 13.5
Detail of diode mounting

Components list for the practice amplifier

Resistors
R1	1MΩ
R2	6.8kΩ
R3	5.6kΩ
R4	270Ω
R5	39kΩ
R6	56kΩ
R7	2.7kΩ
R8	47Ω
R9	1kΩ
R10	680Ω
R11	220Ω
R12	1Ω
R13	1Ω
R14	33Ω
VR1	10kΩ log pot
VR2	22kΩ log pot
VR3	1kΩ min horizontal pre-set

Capacitors
C1	1μF, 10V
C2	470μF, 10V
C3	47μF, 10V
C4	10μF, 10V
C5	0.22μF, polyester
C6	1μF, 10V
C7	220μF, 10V
C8	1000pF, polyester
C9	0.01μF, polyester
C10	1000μF, 25V

Transistors
TR1	BC109C
TR2	BC184L
TR3	BC214L
TR4	BC142
TR5	BC143

Diodes
D1, D2	1N4007

Miscellaneous
S1	SPST switch
L/S	Loudspeaker 8Ω

Matrix board, 0.1in pitch, 36 strips by 37 holes

Using the amplifier

The amplifier may be fitted in a case with its own loudspeaker — a good 8Ω speaker is essential to utilise the full performance of this project. A 7 × 4 elliptical gave good results with the prototype. Leads to the input should be screened, also those to the volume and tone control if they are more than a few inches in length. If hum is a problem when the guitar or other input is unplugged a 100kΩ resistor across the input socket should cure it. A pair of 15Ω stereo headphones were used with the unit, with the socket wired to place them in parallel; the value of R14 proved to be about right for these. Other phones may require a change in value of this resistor for best results.

14

Components, Testing and Boxing-Up

A few notes on the components sued may be helpful to the newcomer to electronics. The resistors used are all ¼W carbon film types, 5% tolerance. These are small, easy to obtain and very cheap. If the use of any other type of resistor is contemplated, the constructor should first make sure it will physically fit into the layout. The electrolytic capacitor voltages quoted are nominal; in the circuits in this book the working voltage is not important so long as it is high enough. All the 1μF capacitors used are in fact 63V types, this being the lowest voltage rating available at the time of construction. Again the physical size is the governing factor.

The 741 op-amp is manufactured by a number of different companies, who use different markings. Thus it may be found as the μA741, LM741, L1741C, etc. No matter, if it is an op-amp and carries the marking 741, that's what it is. It is supplied in three standard packages; the round metal TO99, a 14-pin DIL, and the 8-pin DIL used in this book, which is usually by far the cheapest.

All the components used in the projects in this book came from Maplin Electronic Supplies, whose advertisement may be found in any of the British electronic hobbyists' magazines. Their catalogue is a positive mine of information about the components they supply and is well worth the small price they ask for it.

The circuits in this book were all designed to work from 9V battery supplies; and with the exception of the amplifier and possibly the mini organ they all have a very low power consumption, so a PP3 battery is all that is required by way of a supply. They will all run satisfactorily down to 7V or less, ensuring long battery life and reliable operation.

When first switching on a circuit it is a good idea to have a meter connected in series with the power supply, set to 100mA to allow for the initial brief surge of current as the decoupling capacitors charge up. Most faults likely to damage components cause heavy current consumption, so this can be checked immediately before any further testing is carried out. As a typical example of fault-finding procedure, the rectification of a fault in the fuzz unit was carried out as follows.

Figure 14.1

Testing a transistor with an ohm-meter. A wet finger placed across the base and collector should produce a reading. Note the reversed polarity of the meter leads — on most meters lead polarity reverses on resistance ranges

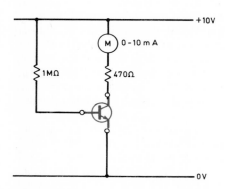

Figure 14.2

Transistor gain testing. Gain may be read directly 0—1000 from the meter. The 470 Ω resistor protects the meter if the transistor is short circuit

After construction, the unit was tested with a guitar and amplifier and simply refused to work; no signals passed through it at all. A quick test with the voltmeter revealed full supply voltage at the collector of TR1, indicating that this transistor was not biased on at all. The resistors were unlikely to be faulty, so the most likely culprits were either C1 or the transistor. C1 was tested simply by removing the input, this made no difference to the collector voltage. TR1 was then removed and tested with the resistance range of the meter, Fig. 14.1 shows how this is done. This test gave a suspicious result, so the circuit of Fig. 14.2 was lashed together to obtain an approximate gain figure. This was found to be only 20 — a suffix C device should have a gain in excess of 400. A replacement transistor cured the problem.

Notes on boxing-up have been given in the individual chapters. Some of the projects may be fitted into existing equipment and do not need cases of their own; for those that do the days when home-built gear had to look home-built are long gone. Ready made cases of all shapes and sizes, made from plastics, steel or alloy, are available from most of the major component suppliers. It is worth remembering in some instances that a metal box affords excellent screening for the circuit it houses. A vast range of knobs are obtainable, and to give a really professional finish, control labelling and other marking may be carried out using instant lettering transfers, which simply rub on with a ball-point pen.

An exception is the amplifier, which will give a much better sound if its loudspeaker is housed in a box made from plywood or chipboard, along the same lines as a bookshelf type hi-fi speaker. The amplifier and battery may be housed in the same case, with controls on the top, making an attractive miniature 'combination' amplifier.

Appendix

Resistor colour code

Most resistors are colour coded to indicate their resistance in ohms and the tolerance (the amount by which the actual value might differ from that marked).

There are four coloured bands around the body of the resistor and the first three give the resistance. The first coloured band (the one nearest the end of the body) corresponds to the first digit, the second colour gives the second digit and the third band tells you how many noughts follow these two digits.

The figures corresponding to the colours are:

black	0
brown	1
red	2
orange	3
yellow	4
green	5
blue	6
violet	7
grey	8
white	9

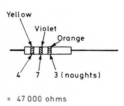

The fourth band indicates the tolerance of the resistor. Only four colours are used here:

silver	10%
gold	5%
red	2%
brown	1%

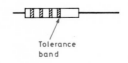

Absence of a fourth band indicates 20% tolerance.

Distinguishing terminals in semiconductors

Although all transistors have terminals that are easily recognised on circuit diagrams, distinguishing them on the actual device isn't always

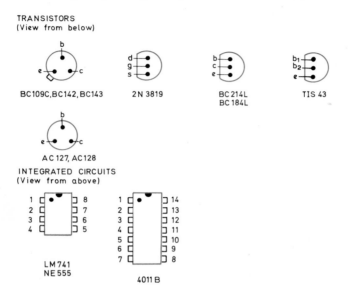

TRANSISTORS
(View from below)

BC109C, BC142, BC143   2N 3819   BC214L
                                   BC184L   TIS 43

AC 127, AC 128

INTEGRATED CIRCUITS
(View from above)

LM 741
NE 555

4011 B

Figure A.1

Terminal identifications for semiconductors used in this book. Transistors show bottom views, i.c.s are top views

quite as simple. The illustration shows the pin identifications for all the transistors circuits used in the projects in this book.

Also shown is the numbering convention adopted for i.c.s in 8-pin DIL and 14-pin DIL packages. Transistor illustrations are viewed from below and i.c. illustrations are viewed from above.